THANKS

Sincere thanks to everyone who helped me
write this book. My family and friends who

supported me with advice and motivation.
A group of parents and children in 4th grade
at Engidalsskóli Hafnarfjörður, who read

over the book and answered questions,
also helped in its preparation.

Special thanks to my kids Steinar Bragi and

Anna Jóna for their tremendous help.

The writing of this book tested the following
strengths of the author: creativity,
perspective, courage, resilience,
cooperation, gratitude and hope.

FOR PARENTS

It is good to learn about your strengths early in life.

Children learn and practice new concepts

in this book. They gradually discover more

strengths and become more self aware,

which is good for their esteem. By working with

strengths we get to know ourselves better

and learn to work with ourselves in a new way.

According to psychologists Peterson and Seligman,

who created the VIA Survey of Character Strengths,

there are 24 strengths, which are divided into 6

groups. You can rely on strengths too much and/or

too little, which then creates an imbalance.

WHO AM I? Strengths

Text: © Sigríður Birna Bragadóttir 2021

Translation:: © Steinar Bragi Sigurjónsson 2021

Illustrations: © Anna Jóna Sigurjónsdóttir 2021

Layout & Design: © Hafdís Anna Bragadóttir 2021

Proofreader: Rán Einarsdóttir Henry and Bragi Skúlason

Photo of author: © Þórdís Erla Ágústsdóttir

Publisher: Spurning, Hafnarfjörður, 2021, www.spurning.is

Printing: Amazon Kindle Direct Publishing and IngramSpark

Printed Book: ISBN 978-9935-24-993-7

E-book: ISBN 978-9935-24-994-4

WHO AM I?

Sigríður Birna Bragadóttir

ANNA

Anna is an 8 year old girl who lives in Reykjavik with her parents and Noah, her 9 year old brother. She's in 3rd grade and school has just started after summer break.

She attended an acting course in the summer and really liked it. Anna wants to be an actress when she gets older.

She has many friends at school and likes to play with them.

Anna sometimes watches TV when she comes home from school and sees a cartoon in which the girl claims to have many strengths and weaknesses.

Anna has heard about weaknesses before and knows what they are. But she wants to know more about strengths and therefore asks her parents.

Her mother smiles when Anna asks and says strengths are never discussed enough. Her mother decides to teach Anna a game involving crowns.

The next weekend they go together to
a bookstore and buy all sorts of papers.
When they come home they make
six crowns.

They first experiment with white paper
to practice creating a suitable crown
shape. Then they cut out all the crowns and
staple or tape them together. Anna
and mom admire the beautiful crowns.

The crowns have different colors.

One is **yellow**,

another is **red**,

the third is **green**,

the fourth is **blue**,

the fifth is **purple**,

and the sixth is **orange**.

Anna and mom decide to take a break
and get hot cocoa and donuts.
They enjoy each other's company.

Anna's mother then teaches her a strengths
game. They have six crowns and intend to
learn about six groups of strengths.

They begin with one crown and
then continue on with the next ones.
The strengths sometimes have strange
names, however Anna knows many words.
She's excited to learn about her strengths.

WISDOM

WISDOM TEACHES HOW WE LEARN IN DIFFERENT WAYS AND USE WHAT WE LEARN DIFFERENTLY.

Anna puts on the first crown, called wisdom, which is yellow. She learns about its group of strengths and writes the words on the crown to remember them better.

Curiosity is wanting to know a lot and to try various things.

Creativity is creating things and knowing how they work.

Love of learning is to have fun learning new things.

Judgment is to know the difference between right and wrong.

Perspective is to envision the whole and to see what the situation looks like.

After Anna has learned about the yellow strengths she says she knows what curiosity and creativity are. Mom suggests for Anna to put on the yellow crown and practice curiosity, which she does.

Anna likes to be curious. She feels as if her mind is open and she dares to try new things, think about something different or read about something new.

1

HUMANITY

HUMANITY TEACHES
COMMUNICATIONS STRENGHTS
AND HOW WE ARE
WITH OTHER PEOPLE.

The second crown is called humanity and is red. Anna puts it on, learns about its strengths and writes the words on the crown.

Kindness is being kind to others.

Love is loving and caring for others.

Social skills involve feeling comfortable with people and enjoying talking to others.

The next day, Anna puts on the red crown at home and practices kindness.

She's kind to her dad who's cooking dinner and sets the table.

COURAGE

COURAGE TEACHES
US TO SET GOALS
AND ACHIEVE THEM.

The third crown is called courage and is green. Anna puts on the crown, learns about its strengths and writes the words on it.

Bravery is daring to do various things and be fearless.

Honesty is telling the truth.

Perseverance is to continue even though it may be difficult.

Zest is to be full of life and allow life to give you energy.

Anna tries on the green crown. She practices courage the next day at school and plays ball with the big kids during recess.

JUSTICE

JUSTICE TEACHES US
HOW WE WORK
WITH OTHER PEOPLE.

The fourth crown is called justice and is blue. Anna puts on the crown, learns about its strengths and writes the words on it.

Teamwork is working together in a game or on a mission.

Leadership is being a leader and taking responsibility.

Fairness is doing everything in a fair way for everybody.

Anna tries to practice teamwork at school during group work and likes it.

4

TEMPERANCE

TEMPERANCE TEACHES US
HOW WE ARE WHEN
OTHERS FEEL BAD OR
SOMETHING IS DIFFICULT.

The fifth crown is called temperance and is purple. Anna puts on the crown, learns about its strengths and writes the words on it.

Forgiveness is saying sorry when you have done something wrong.

Prudence is acting with caution and taking care.

Self-Regulation is knowing how to control yourself.

Humility is knowing yourself, but not seeking the spotlight.

Anna decides to think about forgiveness throughout the day.

TRANSCENDENCE

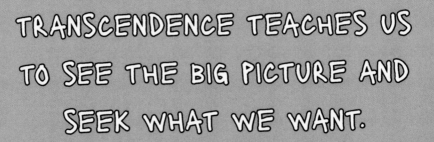

TRANSCENDENCE TEACHES US TO SEE THE BIG PICTURE AND SEEK WHAT WE WANT.

The sixth crown is called transcendence and is orange. Anna puts on the crown, learns about its strengths and writes the words on it.

Humor is to laugh and to make others laugh.

Gratitude is to be thankful and to be happy with what we have.

Hope is to believe in a bright future even when the opposite is true.

Appreciation of beauty is to be able to see what is beautiful around us and what makes us happy.

Spirituality is to search for a spiritual purpose or belief in a higher power.

Noah, Anna's brother, has been watching his sister all week and asks to join in the game. Anna makes a crown for her brother.

Mom suggests they both practice humor. Anna and Noah try different ways to be funny, to make others laugh and feel good. It's fun and they learn a lot about themselves and each other.

It's nice to tell jokes and the siblings laugh a lot. In the evening they talk a lot about strengths and dad remembers that they own a deck of strengths cards.

After dinner, they find the deck of cards so everyone can practice their strengths. The family plays all kinds of games with the cards. Everyone chooses their strengths and then they discuss their choices, which is sometimes funny and comes as a surprise.

Anna has now learned about all of the strengths. She thinks there are so many, yet has now practiced them all. She no longer needs to wear a crown to remember the strengths.

ANNA IS SURE SHE WILL
CONTINUE PRACTICING
THE STRENGTHS LIKE A
MUSCLE IN THE BODY THAT
BECOMES STRONGER AND
STRONGER WHEN YOU
EXERCISE OR TRAIN.

HOW ABOUT YOU?

SOURCES

This book relies on the following sources:

Peterson, C., & Seligman, M. E. P (2004). Carachter Strengths and Virtues: A handbook and Classification. Washington, DC: American Psychological Association. The VIA Institute on Charachter. Cincinnati, Ohio. Retrieved from URL: www.viacharacter.com

Waters, L (2017). The Strength Switch. Strength Based Parenting. New York: Penguin Random House.

Made in the USA
Middletown, DE
11 November 2021

52146250R00015